ROCK & POP

TRINITY
COLLEGE LONDON

THE EXAM AT A GLANCE

For your Rock & Pop exam you will need to perform a set of **three songs** and one of the **Session skills** assessments, either **Playback** or **Improvising**. You can choose the order in which you play your set-list.

Song 1

Choose a song from this book

OR from www.trinityrock.com

Song 2

Choose a different song from this book

OR from www.trinityrock.com

OR perform a song you have chosen yourself: this could be your own cover version or a song you have written. It should be at the same level as the songs in this book. See the website for detailed requirements.

Song 3: Technical focus

Choose one of the Technical focus songs from this book, which cover three specific technical elements.

Session skills

Choose either **Playback** or **Improvising**.

When you are preparing for your exam please check on **www.trinityrock.com** for the most up-to-date information and requirements as these can change from time to time.

CONTENTS

Tuning track: E, A, D, G with a pause between each note.

Trinity College London's Rock & Pop syllabus and supporting publications have been devised and produced in association with Faber Music and Peters Edition London.

Trinity College London
Registered office:
89 Albert Embankment
London SE1 7TP UK
T + 44 (0)20 7820 6100
F + 44 (0)20 7820 6161
E music@trinitycollege.co.uk
www.trinitycollege.co.uk

Registered in the UK. Company no. 02683033
Charity no. 1014792
Patron HRH The Duke of Kent KG

Copyright © 2012 Trinity College London
Second impression, March 2013

Cover and book design by Chloë Alexander
Brand development by Andy Ashburner @ Caffeinehit (www.caffeinehit.com)
Photographs courtesy of Rex Features Limited.
Printed in England by Caligraving Ltd

Audio produced, mixed and mastered by Tom Fleming
Bass arranged by Tom Fleming
Backing tracks arranged by Tom Fleming
Musicians
Vocals: Bo Walton, Brendan Reilly & Alison Symons
Keyboards: Oliver Weeks
Guitar: Tom Fleming
Bass: Ben Hillyard
Drums: George Double
Studio Engineer: Joel Davies www.thelimehouse.com

All rights reserved

ISBN: 978-0-85736-227-8

YOUR PAGE NOTES

SONGS — BLITZKRIEG BOP

Ramones

Words and Music by Joey Ramone, Johnny Ramone,
Dee Dee Ramone and Tommy Ramone

Use this song as a speed challenge! Try to increase speed while relaxing your hand

♩ = 160 **Punk Rock** *2 bars count-in*

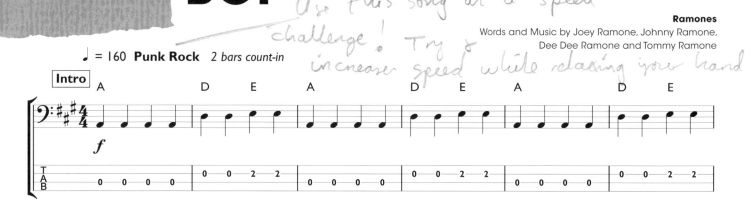

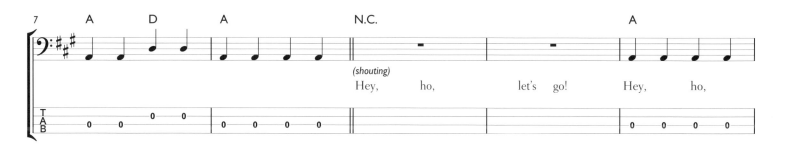

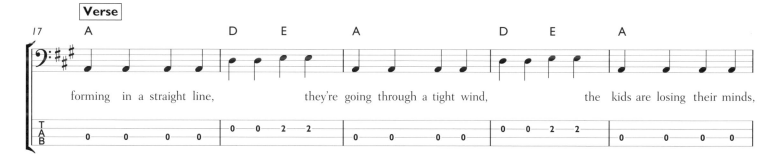

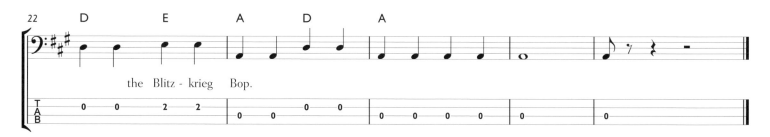

SONGS FOLSOM PRISON BLUES

Johnny Cash
Words and Music by John R. Cash

Please work through this piece – make sure to use 'walking ...

www.trinityrock.com

SONGS NO SURPRISES

Radiohead
Words and Music by Thomas Yorke, Jonathan Greenwood,
Colin Greenwood, Edward O'Brien and Philip Selway

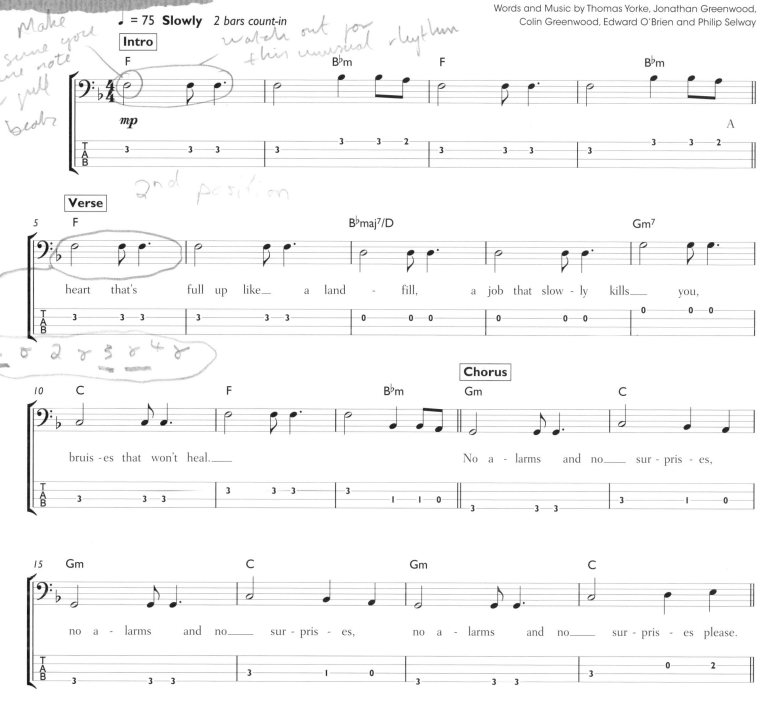

SONGS BLACK BETTY

TRACK 8 demo • TRACK 9 backing

Lead Belly
New Words and New Music Arrangement by Huddie Ledbetter

♩ = 88 **Blues Rock** *2 bars count-in*

Intro — N.C. — *whole song in 1st position*

Bass drum & guitar for 2 bars

Chorus — E5 — mf

Whoa,___ Black Bet - ty, bam - ba - lam, whoa,___

Use rest-stroke picking throughout

A5 — E5 — Verse I — N.C.

___ Black Bet - ty, bam - ba - lam. She's from Birm - ing - ham,___ bam - ba - lam, way down in

finger 3rd   1st

E5 — N.C.

Alabam', bam - ba - lam. The way she shake that thing, oh she make me sing, whoa,___

Chorus — E5 — A5 — E5

___ Black Bet - ty, bam - ba - lam, whoa,___ Black Bet - ty, bam - ba - lam. Look - y

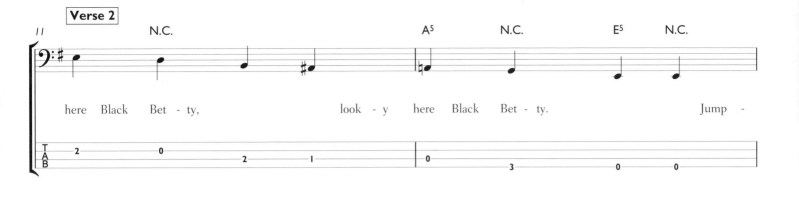

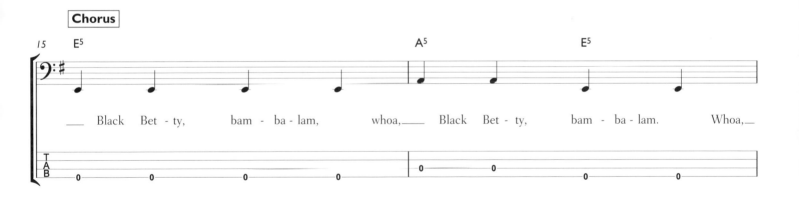

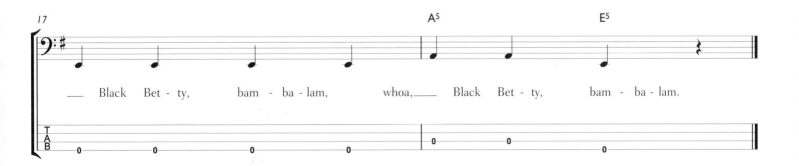

I AM THE MUSIC MAN

In your exam, you will be assessed on the following elements:

1 Dynamics

'I Am The Music Man' has two dynamic markings. At the beginning, the song is marked *mf* (*mezzo forte* which means moderately loud). In the last two bars, it is marked *f*, which means *forte*, or loud. Make sure you show the difference between *mf* and *f*.

2 Counting rests

The bass rests in bars 17 and 18 – count these bars carefully (**1** 2 3 4 **1** 2 3 4) and listen to the backing track so that you come back in at exactly the right place.

There are **o** in bars 19 and 20. These last for four beats so make sure that you hold them on right until the end of the bar. Count carefully.

3 Rhythmic control

Learn the outro well so that you can concentrate on playing in time. Make sure that you hit the last two notes accurately – this will give the song a really strong finish. Look out for the accents (>) on these notes. Make sure that the accented notes are louder than the others.

Practise the outro several times, slowly at first and then gradually build up the speed once the rhythm feels safe:

TECHNICAL FOCUS SONGS

BAND OPTION

I AM THE MUSIC MAN

Black Lace
Trad

♩ = 92 **Pop**   *2 bars count-in*

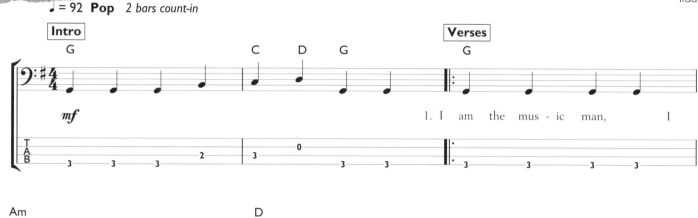

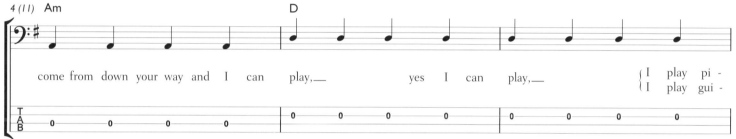

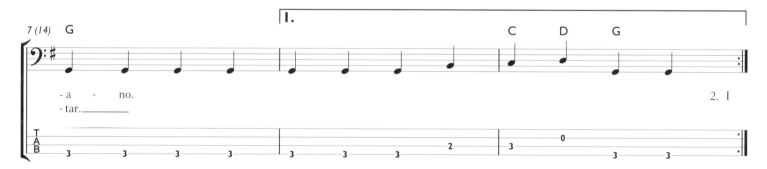

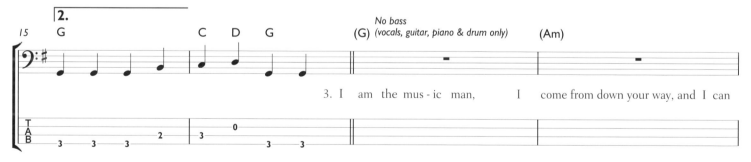

YOU DON'T LOVE ME

In your exam, you will be assessed on the following technical elements:

1 Rhythmic control

The bass plays the same rhythm throughout 'You Don't Love Me'. Mastering this rhythm should help you play the whole song. Make sure that you keep a steady rhythm throughout. Practise it slowly at first and then gradually build up the speed once the rhythm feels secure:

The main beats fall on the first and third beats of each bar. Try to emphasise these notes slightly.

2 Muting

The fretting hand has very little to do in this song – apart from one bar, the whole song is played on open strings. This means you can put your fretting hand to good use muting strings (touching strings lightly to stop them ringing once the note has ended).

3 Counting rests

This song opens with one bar's rest. You will need to count **1 2 3 4** so that you come in at the right place.

YOU DON'T LOVE ME

Dawn Penn
Words and Music by Willie C Cobbs

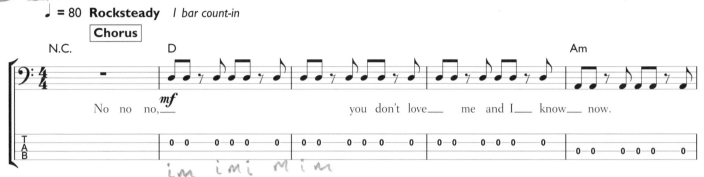

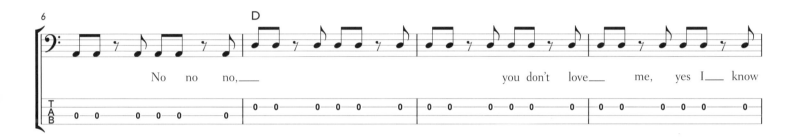

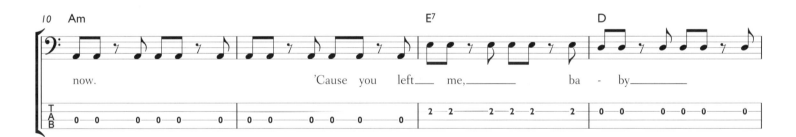

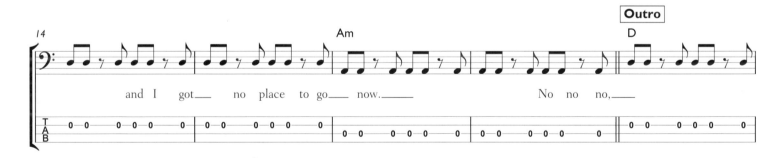

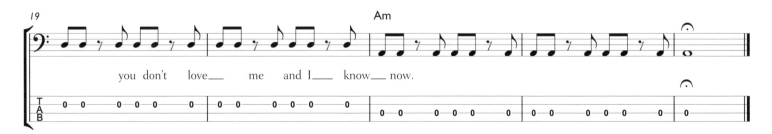

BLITZKRIEG BOP

Ramones

'Blitzkrieg Bop' was released in 1977 as the Ramones' first single and later included on their debut album *Ramones*.

The Ramones were an American punk band – some people say the first ever punk band – famous for their appearances at the iconic CBGB club in New York. Their music has many of the hallmarks of punk music – short energetic songs over simple chord progressions, often played at breakneck speed, with distortion and feedback and a raucous half-shouting style of singing.

'Blitzkrieg Bop' is loud and energetic. It has the dynamic marking f at the beginning; this stands for *forte*, which means play loudly.

You will need to put lots of energy into your performance, at the same time as keeping the rhythm tight. Keep listening to the backing track to make sure that you are staying in time.

The rests in bars 9–10 are important:
- Keep counting **1** 2 3 4, **1** 2 3 4 in your head to make sure that you come in at the right place – it is tempting to rush.
- Mute your strings to make the rest really silent.

Your final note is a ♪ – to make a really tight, punchy ending to the song, make sure that this last note is played short and is not left to ring on.

PERFORMANCE · HINTS & TIPS ·

'*The* kids are *losing* their *minds*'

FOLSOM PRISON BLUES

Johnny Cash

The American singer-songwriter Johnny Cash (1932–2003) was the son of a poor cotton farmer in Arkansas. He was a country-influenced singer with an unmistakable voice – a deep, distinctive bass-baritone. His songs, which he started writing when he was only 12, often use themes taken from the harsher side of life – divorce, prison, murder and war.

'Folsom Prison Blues' was one of Johnny Cash's first recordings and was released in the 1950s. He felt a great compassion for prisoners and gave many concerts in gaols, always opening with this song.

PERFORMANCE · HINTS & TIPS ·

'Folsom Prison Blues' has the dynamic marking **_mf_** at the beginning; this stands for *mezzo forte* which means play moderately loudly.

The song opens with one bar's rest. Listen for the guitar cue which is printed on your music – it will help you to come in at the right place.

The most important element to master in this song is the two-beat feel. Play strong, heavy ♩ notes with clean rests in-between. The overall effect should be bouncy and energetic. Look out for passages like bar 16 where the bass plays an extra note – these add interest and momentum to the music.

Bring the song to a convincing close by making the last note short and definite.

'I ain't *seen the* sunshine *since I don't know* when'

NO SURPRISES

Radiohead

'No Surprises' is taken from Radiohead's 1997 album *OK Computer*. The band, whose music is sometimes described as 'intelligent rock', is not afraid to experiment and takes influences not just from rock music, but also from contemporary classical, jazz, electronic and film music.

OK Computer is a sophisticated album, with subtle rhythms, complex syncopations, and distorted guitars all helping to create unusual textures and atmospheres. 'No Surprises' combines world-weary lyrics with an almost child-like music-box accompaniment.

PERFORMANCE • HINTS & TIPS •

The mood of this song is melancholy and restrained. It has the dynamic marking *mp* at the beginning; this stands for *mezzo piano* which means play moderately quietly.

The rhythm used in the first bar of 'No Surprises' recurs throughout the song, so make sure you get this rhythm right before learning the whole song. For a really impressive performance, play the second note of this rhythm a little shorter so that it is slightly detached from the note after it. This will add interest to the bass line. All the other notes in the song should be played *legato*, with each note smoothly moving to the next.

Watch out for the pause (⌢) at the end of this song. Hold this chord longer than four beats.

'A heart *that's* full up like a *landfill*'

BLACK BETTY

Lead Belly

'Black Betty' is an African-American worksong (an early type of black American music sung rhythmically while doing manual labour). Nobody really knows who Black Betty was, but many believe that the name was slang for a prison bullwhip or a bottle of whisky.

'Black Betty' is normally credited to Lead Belly, although he was not the first to record it. Born Huddie Ledbetter, Lead Belly was a wandering musician who spent more than one spell in prison, including a long stretch for murder. His talent as a folk-blues singer and 12-string guitarist was recognised by the folk-music researcher and collector John Lomax, who later secured his release from prison (although he was soon back inside for assault).

Lead Belly's songs have been recorded by Pete Seeger, Lonnie Donegan, The Fall and Nick Cave. The most famous recording of 'Black Betty' was by Ram Jam – it was their only hit.

PERFORMANCE · HINTS & TIPS ·

'Black Betty' opens with two bars' rest for the bass. Listen to the bass drum in the intro – it plays two bars of straight ♩ beats that help you come in on time.

Keep the rhythm tight with the other parts on the backing track. It is particularly important to keep the bass and drums steady and together. This gives a strong rhythmic backbone for the other musicians to play over.

For a really good performance, mute open strings after you've played them. An open string can ring on for a long time – if you hear this happening, touch the ringing string lightly to end the note and clean up the sound.

'Oh *she* make me *sing*'

I AM THE MUSIC MAN

Black Lace

The origins of 'I Am The Music Man' are uncertain. It is usually sung as an action song where the singers act out playing the different instruments and sometimes imitate the sound of the instruments as well. In 1990 it was recorded by the British pop group Black Lace.

PERFORMANCE · HINTS & TIPS ·

'I Am The Music Man' opens with a two-bar figure played by the whole band. Work on this so you can play it confidently and in time with the backing track. Look out for the same figure at the ends of the verses.

Concentrate on keeping in time with the drums in the verses. This will help to give the song a strong rhythmic foundation.

'I can *play* yes I *can* play'

YOU DON'T LOVE ME

Dawn Penn

'You Don't Love Me' was a 1967 rocksteady hit for Dawn Penn. She recorded the song while she was only 15 and still at high school in Kingston, Jamaica. It was produced by Clement 'Sir Coxsone' Dodd, the influential Jamaican record producer.

1960s Jamaican music has had a big influence on mainstream pop music across the world – ska, rocksteady and reggae all originated there. Rocksteady is an early version of reggae – both have an offbeat feel that stresses beats 2 and 4 of the bar.

'You Don't Love Me' has been sampled and covered by many singers, including Rihanna.

PERFORMANCE · HINTS & TIPS ·

This song opens with one bar's rest. You will need to count (1 2 3 4) so that you come in at the right place.

'You Don't Love Me' has the dynamic marking *mf* at the beginning; this stands for *mezzo forte* which means play moderately loudly.

Watch out for the pause (𝄐) at the end of this song. Hold this chord on longer than four beats.

'*... and I got no place to go now, no no no*'

SESSION SKILLS PLAYBACK

For your exam, you can choose either Playback or Improvising (see page 22).
If you choose Playback, you will be asked to play some music you have not seen or heard before.

In the exam, you will be given the song chart and the examiner will play a recording of the music. You will hear several two-bar phrases on the recording: you should play each of them straight back in turn. There's a rhythm track going throughout, which helps you keep in time. There should not be any gaps in the music.

In the exam you will have two chances to play with the recording:
- First time – for practice
- Second time – for assessment.

You should listen to the audio, copying what you hear; you can also read the music. Here are some practice song charts – which are also on the CD in this book.

Don't forget that the Playback test can include requirements which may not be shown in these examples, including those from earlier grades. Check the parameters at www.trinityrock.com to prepare everything which might come up in your exam.

'*I* really *like* the *way* music *looks* on *paper*. It *looks* like *art* to *me*'

Steve Vai

Practice playback 1

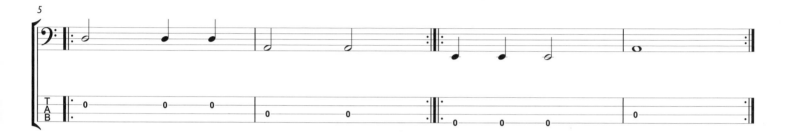

Practice playback 2

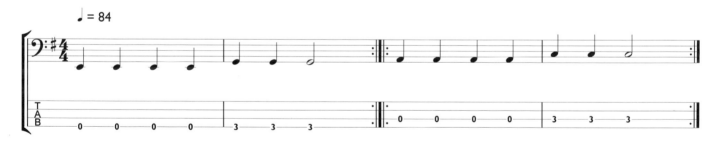

SESSION SKILLS

IMPROVISING

For your exam, you can choose either Playback (see page 20), or Improvising.
If you choose to improvise, you will be asked to improvise over a backing track that you haven't heard before in a specified style.

In the exam, you will be given a song chart and the examiner will play a recording of the backing track. The backing track consists of a passage of music played on a loop. You should improvise a bass line which fits the track.

In the exam you will have two chances to play with the recording:
- First time – for practice
- Second time – for assessment.

Here are some improvising charts for practice which are also on the CD in this book.

Don't forget that the Improvising test can include requirements which may not be shown in these examples, including those from earlier grades. Check the parameters at www.trinityrock.com to prepare everything which might come up in your exam.

Practice improvisation 1

♩ = 120 **Rock**

| Em | Am | Em | Em |

Practice improvisation 2

♩ = 90 **Pop**

| D | A | D | D |

HELP PAGES

CHOOSING A SONG FOR YOUR EXAM

There are lots of options to help you choose your three songs for the exam.
For Songs 1 and 2, you can choose a song which is:

- from this book
- from www.trinityrock.com

Or for Song 2 you can choose a song which is:

- sheet music from a printed or online source.
- your own arrangement of a song or a song you have written yourself (see page 24).

You can play the song unaccompanied or with a backing track (minus the bass part). If you like, you can create a backing track yourself (or with friends), or you could add your own vocals – or both.

For Initial, the song should be between 30 seconds and two minutes long, and the level of difficulty should be similar to your other songs.
When choosing a song, think about:

- Does it work on my instrument?
- Are there any technical elements that are too difficult for me?
  (If so, perhaps save it for when you do the next grade.)
- Do I enjoy playing it?
- Does it work with my other songs to create a good set-list?

See www.trinityrock.com for information and advice on choosing your own song.

SHEET MUSIC

You must always bring an original copy of the book or a download sheet with email certificate for each song you perform in the exam. If you choose to write your own song you must provide the examiner with a copy of the sheet music. Your music can be:

- a lead sheet with lyrics, chords and melody line
- a chord chart with lyrics
- a full score using conventional staff notation
- see page 24 for details on presenting a song you have written yourself.

The title of the song and your name should be on the sheet music.

WRITING YOUR OWN SONG

You can play a song that you have written yourself for one of the choices in your exam. For Initial, your song should last between 30 seconds and two minutes, so it is likely to be quite straightforward. It is sometimes difficult to know where to begin, however. Here are some suggestions for starting points:

- **A melody**: many songs are made up around a 'hook' (a short catchy melodic idea, usually only a few notes long).
Try writing a couple of ideas for hooks here:

- **A chord sequence**: a short chord sequence can provide an entire verse or chorus. Write your ideas for a chord sequence here:

- **A rhythm**: a short repeated rhythm will often underpin an entire song.
Think of a couple of short rhythms you could use here:

There are plenty of other ways of starting: perhaps with a riff or a lyric, for example.

You will also need to consider the **structure** of your song (verse and chorus, 12-bar blues, and so on), the **style** it is in (blues, hard rock, etc.), and what **instruments** it is for (e.g. voice/keyboards/drums . . .).

There are many choices to be made – which is why writing a song is such a rewarding thing to do.

WRITING YOUR SONG DOWN

Rock and pop music is often written as a **lead sheet** with the lyrics (if there are any), chords and a melody line.

- As a bass player, you may want to write your part on a **five-line stave** or as **tab**. Both have been used for the songs in this book

- You can, if you prefer, use a **graph** or **table** to represent your music, as long as it is clear to anyone else (including the examiner) how the song goes.

PLAYING IN A BAND

Playing in a band is exciting: it can be a lot of fun and, as with everything, the more you do it, the easier it gets. It is very different from playing on your own. Everyone contributes to the overall sound: the most important skill you need to develop is listening.

For a band to sound good, the players need to be 'together' – that mainly means keeping in time with each other, but also playing at the same volume, and with the same kind of feeling.

Your relationship with the other band members is also important. Talk with them about the music you play, the music you like, and what you'd like the band to achieve short-term and long-term.

Band rehearsals are important – you should not be late, tired or distracted by your mobile phone! Being positive makes a huge difference. Try to create a friendly atmosphere in rehearsals so that everybody feels comfortable trying out new things. Don't worry about making mistakes: that is what rehearsals are for.

'Black Betty' (page 8) and 'I Am The Music Man' (page 11) are arranged for band. You will find parts for vocals, keyboards, guitar and drums in the other Trinity Rock & Pop Initial books or available online. Trinity offers exams for groups of musicians at various levels. The songs arranged for bands are ideal to include as part of a set-list for these exams. Have a look at the website for more details.

HINTS AND TIPS

- When you are starting out, it is easier if you have only one of each instrument, so that you can hear clearly what everybody is playing.

- Record your practice sessions and listen back for sections that worked well and bits that had problems.

- Meet up regularly to socialise before and after rehearsals to help keep in touch with each other.

PLAYING WITH BACKING TRACKS

The CD contains demos and backing tracks of all the songs in the book. The additional songs at www.trinityrock.com also come with demos and backing tracks.

- In your exam, you should perform with the backing track, or you can create your own (see below).
- The backing tracks begin with a click track, which sets the tempo and helps you start accurately.
- Be careful to set the balance between the volume of the backing track and your instrument.
- Listen carefully to the backing track to ensure you are playing in time.

If you are creating your own backing track here are some further tips:
- Make sure the sound quality is of a good standard.
- Think carefully about the instruments/sounds you are putting on the backing track.
- Avoid copying what you are playing on the backing track – it should support not duplicate.
- Do you need to include a click track at the beginning?

COPYRIGHT IN A SONG

If you are a singer or songwriter it is important to know about copyright. When someone writes a song or creates an arrangement they own the copyright (sometimes called 'the rights') to that version. The copyright means that other people cannot copy it, sell it, perform it in a concert, make it available online or record it without the owner's permission or the appropriate licence. When you write a song you automatically own the copyright to it, which means that other people cannot copy your work. But just as importantly, you cannot copy other people's work, or perform it in public without their permission or the appropriate licence.

Points to remember
- You can create a cover version of a song for an exam or other non-public performance.
- You cannot record your cover version and make your recording available to others (by copying it or uploading it to a website) without the appropriate licence.
- You own the copyright of your own original song, which means that no one is allowed to copy it.
- You cannot copy someone else's song without their permission or the appropriate licence.
- If you would like to use somebody else's words in your own song you must check if they are in copyright and, if so, we recommend you confirm with the author that they are happy for the words to be used as lyrics.
- Materials protected by copyright can normally be used as lyrics in our examinations as these are private performances under copyright law. The examiner may ask you the name of the original author in the exam.
- When you present your own song to the examiner make sure you include the title, the names of any writers and the source of your lyrics.

NOTES

7 Nation Army

A

```
2   2 0 2 0       3 2
```

B

```
2   2 0 2 0     3 0 3 2
```

Play   A A B A

then

```
3 3 3 3 3 3 3 3 | 5 5 5 5 5 5 5 5
```

ALSO AVAILABLE

Trinity College London Rock & Pop examinations 2012-2017 are also available for:

Bass Initial
ISBN: 978-0-85736-227-8

Bass Grade 1
ISBN: 978-0-85736-228-5

Bass Grade 2
ISBN: 978-0-85736-229-2

Bass Grade 3
ISBN: 978-0-85736-230-8

Bass Grade 4
ISBN: 978-0-85736-231-5

Bass Grade 5
ISBN: 978-0-85736-232-2

Bass Grade 6
ISBN: 978-0-85736-233-9

Bass Grade 7
ISBN: 978-0-85736-234-6

Bass Grade 8
ISBN: 978-0-85736-235-3

Keyboards Initial
ISBN: 978-0-85736-236-0

Keyboards Grade 1
ISBN: 978-0-85736-237-7

Keyboards Grade 2
ISBN: 978-0-85736-238-4

Keyboards Grade 3
ISBN: 978-0-85736-239-1

Keyboards Grade 4
ISBN: 978-0-85736-240-7

Keyboards Grade 5
ISBN: 978-0-85736-241-4

Keyboards Grade 6
ISBN: 978-0-85736-242-1

Keyboards Grade 7
ISBN: 978-0-85736-243-8

Keyboards Grade 8
ISBN: 978-0-85736-244-5

Drums Initial
ISBN: 978-0-85736-245-2

Drums Grade 1
ISBN: 978-0-85736-246-9

Drums Grade 2
ISBN: 978-0-85736-247-6

Drums Grade 3
ISBN: 978-0-85736-248-3

Drums Grade 4
ISBN: 978-0-85736-249-0

Drums Grade 5
ISBN: 978-0-85736-250-6

Drums Grade 6
ISBN: 978-0-85736-251-3

Drums Grade 7
ISBN: 978-0-85736-252-0

Drums Grade 8
ISBN: 978-0-85736-253-7

Vocals Initial
ISBN: 978-0-85736-254-4

Vocals Grade 1
ISBN: 978-0-85736-255-1

Vocals Grade 2
ISBN: 978-0-85736-256-8

Vocals Grade 3
ISBN: 978-0-85736-257-5

Vocals Grade 4
ISBN: 978-0-85736-258-2

Vocals Grade 5
ISBN: 978-0-85736-259-9

Vocals Grade 6 (female voice)
ISBN: 978-0-85736-263-6

Vocals Grade 6 (male voice)
ISBN: 978-0-85736-260-5

Vocals Grade 7 (female voice)
ISBN: 978-0-85736-264-3

Vocals Grade 7 (male voice)
ISBN: 978-0-85736-261-2

Vocals Grade 8 (female voice)
ISBN: 978-0-85736-265-0

Vocals Grade 8 (male voice)
ISBN: 978-0-85736-262-9

Guitar Initial
ISBN: 978-0-85736-218-6

Guitar Grade 1
ISBN: 978-0-85736-219-3

Guitar Grade 2
ISBN: 978-0-85736-220-9

Guitar Grade 3
ISBN: 978-0-85736-221-6

Guitar Grade 4
ISBN: 978-0-85736-222-3

Guitar Grade 5
ISBN: 978-0-85736-223-0

Guitar Grade 6
ISBN: 978-0-85736-224-7

Guitar Grade 7
ISBN: 978-0-85736-225-4

Guitar Grade 8
ISBN: 978-0-85736-226-1